ROBERT FUCHS
CHILDREN'S PIECES

from Op.32 & 47

ABRSM

Published by ABRSM (Publishing) Ltd, a wholly owned subsidiary of ABRSM

INTRODUCTION

Robert Fuchs, the Austrian composer and teacher, was born at Frauenthal in Styria in 1847 and died in Vienna in 1927. He started to study various instruments at an early age; and, when he was eighteen, he moved to Vienna to try and earn a living as an organist, répétiteur and teacher. At the same time he continued his studies at the conservatory, where he himself later taught harmony, theory and counterpoint to a generation of musicians which included Mahler, Sibelius, Wolf and Zemlinsky.

As a composer he is chiefly known for his five Serenades for string orchestra and for his chamber works; but he also composed five symphonies – No.1 in C was highly regarded by Brahms – a piano concerto, two operas, three masses, other choral works and a number of songs.

Among his compositions for piano are various descriptive albums for children. The present selection has been taken from two of these: *Jugendklänge* (Youthful Sounds), Op.32, published in Leipzig in the early 1880's, and from *Jugend-album* (Children's Album), Op.47, published by Simrock in Berlin in 1890. Some minor revisions have been made to the expression marks and dynamics. Additional fingering has been included, as well as some proposed pedal indications. At the end of each piece a metronome mark is suggested, but it is no way authoritative or binding.

Morgenlied
Morning Song

R. FUCHS
Op. 32 No. 1

Einfach [Simply]

AB 1946

Herzeleid
Heartache

Op. 32 No. 2

Ruhig, empfindungsvoll [Calmly, full of feeling]

con Ped.

[♩ = c. 100]

Kindliche Bitte
A Child's Request

Langsam und innig [Slowly and with feeling]

Op. 47 No. 1

Stolzer Reitersmann
Proud Horseman

Op. 47 No. 2

Mütterchen erzählt
Mother tells a Story

Langsam, sehr innig [Slowly, very expressively]

Op. 47 No. 16

Gebet
Prayer

Op. 47 No. 3

Liedchen
A Little Song

Op. 47 No. 4

Lächeln unter Tränen
Smiles after Tears

Op. 47 No. 10

Etwas bewegt [With movement]

Lieb' Schwesterlein
Dear Little Sister

Sehr langsam, innig süss [Very slowly and tenderly]

Op. 32 No. 14

Soldatenmarsch
Soldier's March

Frisch und munter [Brisk and lively]

Op. 47 No. 14

AB 1946

[♩ = c. 116]

Romanze
Romance

Op. 47 No. 13

Ziemlich langsam [Rather slowly]

con Ped.

[♩ = c. 104]

Der Regen rieselt
Drizzling Rain

Sehr ruhig [Very calmly]

Op. 32 No. 11

con Ped.

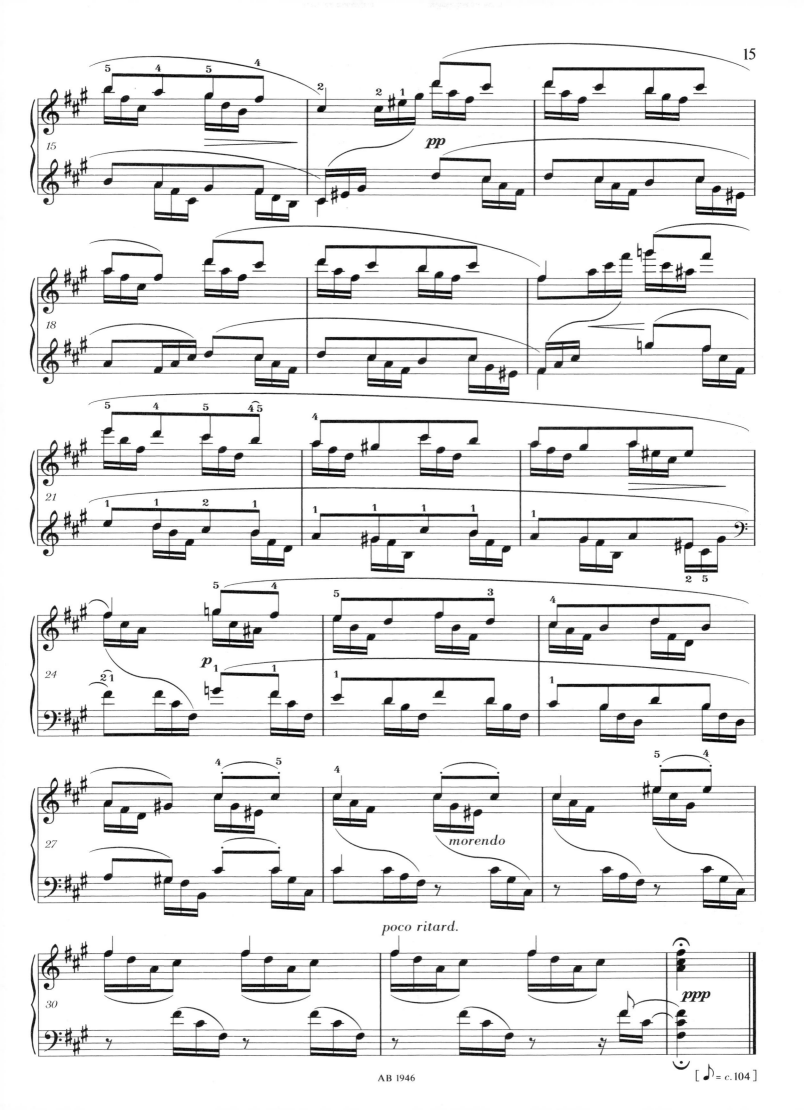

pp

p

morendo

poco ritard.

ppp

[♪ = c.104]

Der kleine Trompeter
The Little Trumpeter

Op. 32 No. 4

AB 1946

Stillvergnügt
Quietly Contented

Innig [With feeling]

Op. 47 No. 6

[♩ = c. 112]

Banges Herzelein
Sad at Heart

Op. 47 No. 5

Etwas bewegt [Not too slow]

Grosses Geheimnis
A Great Mystery

Op. 32 No. 12

Etwas bewegt, sehr zart [Not too slow, but very tenderly]

Abendgebet
Evening Prayer

Langsam, seelenvoll [Slowly, deeply felt]

Op. 32 No. 9

[♩ = c. 66]

Plappermäulchen
Chatterbox

Nicht zu rasch [Not too hurried]

Op. 32 No. 18

AB 1946

$\left[\, \unicode{x2669} = c.\ 72 \,\right]$

Wiegenliedchen
Cradle Song

Op. 47 No. 7

Einfach, zart [Simply and tenderly]

Süsser Trost
Sweet Consolation

Op. 47 No. 11

Zart und innig [Tenderly and expressively]

Stilles Glück
Quiet Happiness

Sehr langsam, innig [Very slowly and expressively]

Op. 47 No. 21

con Ped.

cresc.

rit.

Reproduced and printed by
Halstan & Co. Ltd., Amersham, Bucks., England

AB 1946

[♩ = c. 66]